EGMONT

We bring stories to life

First published in Great Britain in 2011 by Egmont UK Limited
239 Kensington High Street, London W8 6SA
All rights reserved.

© Disney Enterprises, Inc.

Based on the series created by Michael Poryes and Rich Correll & Barry O'Brien
'Sweet Home Hannah Montana' was written by Michael Poryes & Steven Peterman

Text © 2011 Egmont UK Limited
Editor: Catherine Such • Writer: Olivia McLearon
Art Editor/Designer: Amanda Hartley • Editorial Assistant: Hannah Greenfield
Group Editor: Keilly Swift • Group Art Editor: Jeanette Ryall

ISBN 978 1 4052 5693 3
1 3 5 7 9 10 8 6 4 2
Printed in Italy

Disney

HANNAH MONTANA

This annual belongs to

CHRISTOP
GUTRIE H
ER

....
Write your name here.

What's Inside?

Introducing Hannah/Miley!

Welcome to the wonderful world of Miley Stewart ... aka **Hannah Montana!**

Miley by day

Miley Stewart is like most teenage girls, except she's got this totally amazing secret — she's also pop star, Hannah Montana! Miley's managed to keep it from lots of peeps, although her family and BFFs Lilly and Oliver know. And she might have to tell Jackson's new girlfriend, Sienna, too!

Hannah Montana: Popstar!

Miley created her alter ego, Hannah, so she could still live a normal teenage life and not be treated differently at school, just because she's a famous superstar. Clever thinking, huh? Miley once had to go to school as Hannah, which she hated!

Family rules!

Miley lives with her dad Robby Ray and brother Jackson in Malibu, California. She's originally from Tennessee and still has loads of family there. They moved to a ranch at the beginning of season 4.

The BFFs

Miley's BFFs are Lilly and Oliver. At the end of season 3, Oliver left to go touring with the band he had joined. Luckily Lilly's still around and they're having tons of fun together as always — especially since Lilly's moved in with the Stewarts!

Miley VS Hannah

So how is Hannah different from Miley? Miley wears a blonde wig when she's Hannah and has a more funky, glam style! She's also a little bit cheekier when she's rockin' out as Hannah!

Hannah Search

Can you find these Hannah Montana related words in the wordsearch below?

Words go forwards, up, down, diagonally and backwards!

```
G A L O L Y C L O Y Y U
M B U Y M C H H H H Y H B
P V T E R C E S R M E G
E D M R W Y J A T A R E
N I M I B U T Q E A U O
X L G B D I M O G Z G W
Y S O G U H S T G C I E
N R E G N I G N I S B X
H T R A C I N M S Q D G
J G A E U P T J E P X S
T S T W S A N C J N B O
O L P T B I Y I A B R O
```

SINGING	**SECRET**
LOLA	**TRACI**
JUDGE	**ROBBY**
GUITAR	**STAGE**
ACTING	**WIGS**

Answers on page 67.

Six Things

There are six differences in the second picture of Hannah, Lola and Mike. Can you spot them all?

Tick a star when you spot each difference!

1 ✓
2 ✓
3 ☆
4 ✓
5 ✓
6 ✓

Answers on page 67.

11

Get the Look!

Check out Hannah's daytime cool and evening glam. Then follow these tips on how to get the look!

Daytime Casual

Love layers: It's totally Hannah to contrast two different styles – she's twinned her gold cardigan with a pretty floral top here.

Top Tip: Don't be afraid to experiment with contrasting styles. A cropped cardi looks fab over a long Tee.

Belt up: Hannah doesn't always go for clashing colours. This gold belt looks great with her cardigan and sandals!

Top Tip: Choose a base colour for part of your outfit and then choose matching accessories.

Hannah does do casual, but she still likes to bring a bit of glamour to her look with sparkles and metallic colours.

Jean-ius: Miley loves skinny jeans whether she's in Miley mode or has transformed into Hannah. The light grey colour gives them a rock-chick edge!

Top Tip: Skinny jeans look really cool with long, layered tops. You can tuck them into boots in winter too!

When Hannah's on stage she likes to mix it up with a rock chick look and super-glam style.

Hitting the Stage

Pretty in pink: Hannah makes her outfit a little bit girlier with this pink top, which looks awesome with her black shrug!

Top Tip: Pink looks great with black, as well as grey.

Accessorise it: This dangly black necklace adds a sparkly edge to Hannah's look. The bangles look great layered up on each wrist.

Top Tip: Stack up a few bangles in different styles for a fun look.

Statement skirt: Wow! This skirt is rockin'! The ruffles make it perfect for a party too.

Top Tip: You can make a skirt look totally new by wearing it with loads of different tops!

Brill boots: Hannah's boots are fluffy and fun! They're great for performances and for special occasions.

Top Tip: Save your party shoes and just wear them occasionally. It'll make it a real treat when you do put them on!

Miley's Maze mare!

Help Miley get through the maze and past Siena, so that she can get to her Hannah Montana concert on time!

Start

Finish

Answer on page 67.

Sudoku Special!

Put the characters' initials in the right squares to complete the sudoku puzzle!

 **RS**  **LT**  **JS**  **HM**

Answers on page 67.

15

Hannah's Blog

Take a sneaky peek at Hannah's superstar blog!

Back to school!

Today was totally crazy. I mean, I know, I know, my life is pretty crazy at the best of the times, but I registered at Seaview High and went to school today! I wanted to be treated like an ordinary girl but even the principal took a pic of us together on his mobile phone. He claimed he did that with every new student – yeah, right! I tried to convince the other students not to treat me like I was someone special, but it didn't really work ...

Comments (5)

▶ You knew my name, you knew my name, you knew my name, YOU KNEW MY NAME!!!!!!!!!!!!!!!!
Joannie xxx

▶ Hey Hannah, you should have taken your assistant, along – hint hint!
Lola xx

▶ Wow, Hannah Montana at Seaview – wish I'd been there to see it :-)
Oliver xx

▶ If only I went to Seaview!
Mega Hannah fan X

▶ Hey Joannie, it was great to meet you – check out the pic I'm about to put up. Lola, you would have made a great bodyguard! Maybe I'll meet you another time, Oliver ;-). Aww thanks, mega Hannah fan!
Hannah X

Just an ordinary girl

So my experience today of being followed everywhere – yep, even the toilet – and meeting peeps who were so star-struck they couldn't even say my name properly, inspired me to write this new song, 'Ordinary Girl'. I just really wanted to be treated the same as everyone else, but ya know, I guess it was a lot to expect. Hopefully it'll help people realise that we're all the same – seriously, I am just like you guys! Much more than you probably realise ...   Comments (5)

▶ I'M IN A PIC ON YOUR BLOG!!!!!!
Joannie xxx

▶ AND YOU LIKED MY TOP. SERIOUSLY, I'M NEVER CHANGING THIS TOP!
Sarah xxxxxxxxxxxxxx

▶ I can't wait to hear 'Ordinary Girl'. Great to meet you today, Hannah!! Sorry if most peeps were a bit starry-eyed, but can you blame them?!
Lilly xx

▶ You too, Lilly! Joannie, remember what I just said about being an ordinary girl! And Sarah, if you never change your top, won't it start to ... smell a lil' bit?!
Hannah X

▶ OK, good point, Hannah. I can't believe you just replied to my comment – WOW!!!!
Sarah xxxxxxxxxxxxxxxxx

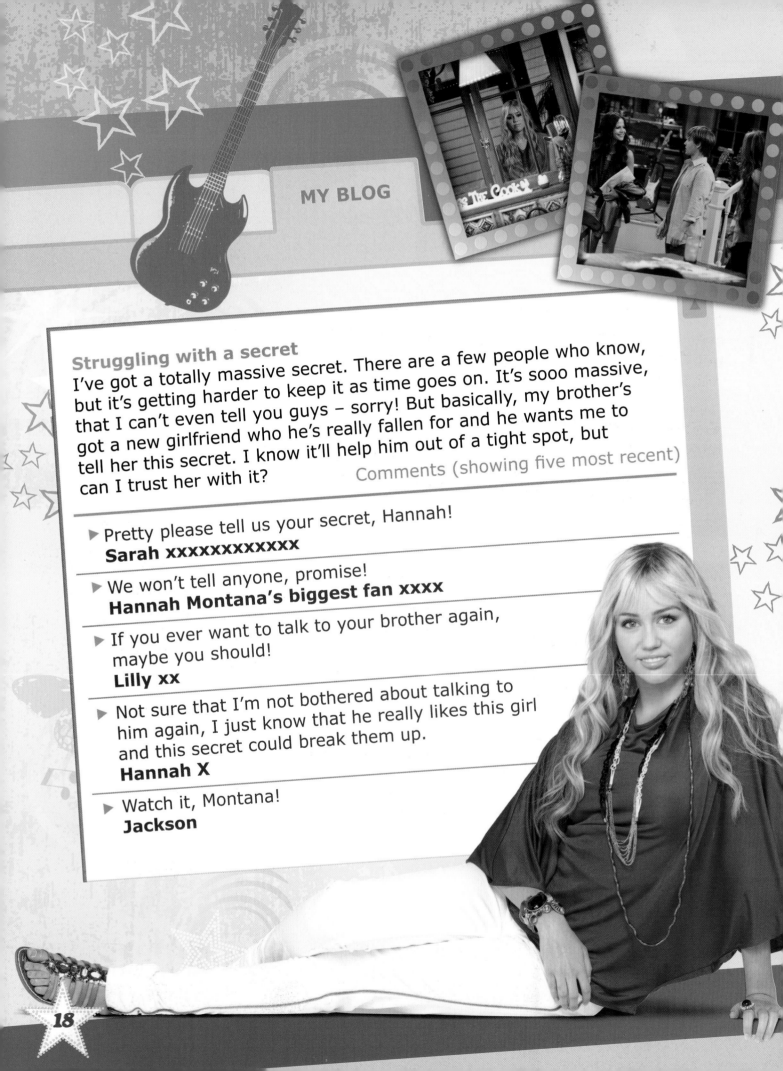

MY BLOG

Struggling with a secret

I've got a totally massive secret. There are a few people who know, but it's getting harder to keep it as time goes on. It's sooo massive, that I can't even tell you guys – sorry! But basically, my brother's got a new girlfriend who he's really fallen for and he wants me to tell her this secret. I know it'll help him out of a tight spot, but can I trust her with it?

Comments (showing five most recent)

▶ Pretty please tell us your secret, Hannah!
Sarah xxxxxxxxxxxx

▶ We won't tell anyone, promise!
Hannah Montana's biggest fan xxxx

▶ If you ever want to talk to your brother again, maybe you should!
Lilly xx

▶ Not sure that I'm not bothered about talking to him again, I just know that he really likes this girl and this secret could break them up.
Hannah X

▶ Watch it, Montana!
Jackson

It's complicated

OK, so my brother's girlfriend is threatening to break up with him over me, so I've really got to tell her this secret, right? I tried to, but then she let slip this little secret about him and it just came out so easily – so how can I trust her with my secret?

Comments (2)

▶ Maybe it was a mistake?!!
Jackson

▶ What you need to do, is tell her and then find out a big secret about her and threaten to expose it, unless she keeps yours!
Lilly xx

Secret: over and out

So I told the secret today and I think the girlfriend might keep it. I was kinda forced into it when my BFF blurted it out by mistake!! But ya know, whatever will be, will be. I just have to trust that she won't tell anyone. Thanks for your support everyone and sorry I couldn't tell you all what the secret was. Watch this space though, cos maybe one day I'll tell y'all …

Comments (2)

▶ I'm sure your brother is **VERY** grateful, Hannah!
Jackson

▶ And I'm sure your BFF feels really, really bad about spilling your secret!
Lilly xx

Superstar Say What?!

Can you match the quote to the right character? We've added clues to help you out!

1

"I'm part of the video game generation! I can't handle long and slow, I need short and fast!"

Clue: Desperate to impress, this character said this as they struggled to read a classic book!

2

"That girl's meltin' for you like butter on a stack of flapjacks!"

Clue: Who gave Jackson this advice? It was someone close to home!

3

"I am gonna be the social hub of senior year!"

Clue: Someone was about to be very disappointed by their new room!

20

A to Z of Hannah Montana

Check out the A to Z of everything that's totally Hannah Montana!

A is for Aunt Dolly
Aunt Dolly is Miley's glamorous stepmother!

B is for Blue Jeans
Robby Ray arranged for Miley's beloved horse, Blue Jeans, to come to Malibu when Miley was super homesick. Aww!

Blue Jeans is back!

C is for Carrots
Miley totally hates carrots!

D is for Dentist
Miley has a massive fear of the dentist – especially this temporary one!

Not terrifying at all!

E is for 'Every Part of Me'
This fab song from 'Miley says Goodbye?, Part 1' makes us blub every time we hear it!

F is for Family
Miley's really close to her family, even though Jackson drives her mad at times!

Miley, her bro and pa

G is for 'Got to Get Her Out of My House'
Lilly drove Miley up the wall in this hilarious episode, when she convinced the Stewarts to let her be their cleaner!

H is for 'Hannah's Gonna Get This'
A totally 'mazing episode from 'Hannah Montana Forever!'

I is for Iyaz
The awesome singer Iyaz sang the duet 'Gonna Get This' with Hannah.

J is for Jake
Miley's ex boyfriend. Luckily Jesse helped her get over him.

Not so great, Jake

K is for 'Killing Me Softly with His Height'
Miley learnt that it's what's inside that counts, in this brilliant episode, where she dates a shorter guy called Connor.

Small, dark & handsome

L is for Lilly
Miley's totally fabulous BFF, Lilly Trustcott!

M is for **Mikayla**
Hannah's pop star rival, Mikayla can't stand Hannah, but likes Miley! Although they pretend that they're friends when they're in public together!

N is for **"No way…**
you are dating that kite-cutting, balloon-popping wart on a big monkey butt!" Another hilarious one-liner from Lilly!

O is for **Oliver Oken**
Miley and Lilly's other BFF — or Ollie-pop as Lilly likes to call him!

P is for **'Promma Mia'**
Remember when Miley went to the prom with the school nerd, Aaron, in this awesome season 3 episode?

Q is for **'Que Sera'**
A really cool song from 'Hannah Montana Forever!'

R is for **Rico's Surf Shack**
Rico's super brains and super-rich family mean that he's already got his own shop — Rico's Surf Shack.

It's Rico time!

S is for **Sweet Niblets**
One of Miley's ace catchphrases!

T is for **'The Best of Both Worlds'**
Hannah's fabulous theme tune which sums up her crazy life!

U is for **Uncle Earl**
Miley's uncle's full of funny stories, including the time he fell off a horse and it took four peeps to help him up — yikes!

W is for **wigs**
Hannah totally rocks a cool blonde wig!

V is for **(Traci) Van Horn**
Traci is Hannah's friend, rather than Miley's friend! Although her and Jake pranked Hannah by pretending to get married in Las Vegas!

Hilarious joke, guys!

X is for **eX Factor**
Miley has a few ex boyfs, but has yet to find her one true love … could it be Jesse?

Y is for **'You Give Lunch a Bad Name'**
Mawmaw took on a job as Seaview High's lunch lady in this giggle-tastic episode!

Z is for **Zzz**
With Hannah's hectic lifestyle, she treasures the moments she gets to sleep in her awesome bedroom!

Here's Lilly ...

Lilly Truscott is one of Miley's BFFs. She's fun-loving, fearless and has a brilliant alter ego called Lola Luftnagle!

It's Lilly

Lilly has been best friends with Miley since the 6th grade and is one of the trusted few who knows who Hannah Montana really is! She was a massive fan of Hannah Montana before she knew the secret – and she still is!

Lilly makes us LOL

Lilly's into loadsa stuff including skateboarding, surfing, hockey and cheerleading. She's not so hot at doing impressions of people, although her attempt at pretending to be a young Hannah Montana fan in 'Hannah's Gonna Get This' was hilarious!

and Lola!

We love Lola!

Lilly has an ace way of helping Miley keep her secret. She poses as Hannah's assistant, the wig-tastic, Lola Luftnagle at Hannah Montana events and concerts! Sooo cool!

Lilly-pop

Awww! Love blossomed between Lilly and Oliver when Miley was away filming a movie. Their relationship isn't without its ups and downs though — they once split up when they had an argument over their favourite bands!

Living it up with the Stewarts!

It's totally awesome that Lilly and Miley now live together! Lilly moved in with the Stewarts when her mom moved to another part of the country, but she drove Miley mad to begin with! Luckily they made up though — phew!

Let's go Code

Use the code to crack the answers to the awesome crossword!

Crazy

The alphabet key: A B C D E F G H I / J K L M N O P Q / R S T U V W X Y Z with picture symbols.

Across

1 Hannah's amazing duet with Iyaz

3 Lori's job

4 Lilly's surname

5 Jackson has real trouble saying this word!

7 Oliver's alter ego is called Mike

III

11 Miley's horse is called

12 Complete the episode title

TENDER

13 Super-small and super-smart guy!

14 Hannah's rival who pretends to be her friend!

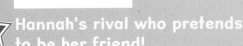

Down

2 Miley and her dad love saying this!

6 Episode with two parts.

MILEY SAYS

7 "You think I'm super!" Which song's this lyric from?

8 He's Miley's boyfriend in season 4

9 Miley's scared of the dentist and

10 Hannah's friend is called Traci

How to be Hannah's BFF!

Wanna find out how to be Hannah's BFF? Follow these tips, but sssh ... don't tell Lola or Mike!

Don't be starstruck!

OK, so she's a world famous pop superstar, but that doesn't mean you should act any different around her. Like Hannah sings herself, she's just an ordinary girl — so make sure you treat her like one!

Keep it secret

If you're BFFs with Hannah, you need to be able to keep her real identity a secret! So let her know that she can trust you by keeping anything she tells you in confidence, to yourself. Don't even tell your diary!

Make her LOL!

It's not just Miley who loves a giggle, her alter ego Hannah is always having a laugh too. Be fun, make jokes and do crazy impressions, and Hannah'll love you for it!

Glam it up!

Hannah Montana is totally glamorous and always looks pop star ready! You've gotta have a passion for fashion and be ready to hit the shops if you wanna be her BFF.

Be there for her

Like any brilliant BFF, make sure you're there for Hannah when she needs you. Living the celebrity lifestyle can be tiring and quite lonesome when you're away from home, so make sure she knows she can call you up for a chat to cheer her up!

Hannah's top tips for being an ace BFF:

1 Be honest:
Lilly and Miley haven't always told each other straightaway when they've been upset with each other, but it's best to get it out in the open and sort it out pronto!

3 Have fun:
Ya know, BFFs who can giggle together are more likely to stay BFFs forever! So make sure you have a laugh with your BFF, as often as you can!

2 Show your love:
It's not all about buying presents and spending lots of money. Make a scrapbook about your friendship, make them a cool card to say how amazing they are or start a cool blog together!

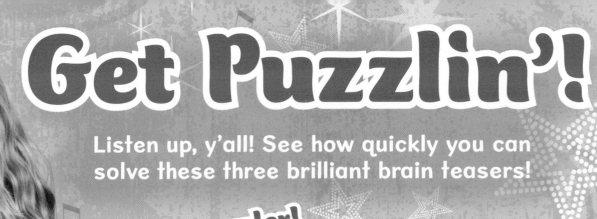

Get Puzzlin'!

Listen up, y'all! See how quickly you can solve these three brilliant brain teasers!

Jigsaw puzzler!

Can you work out which pieces finish this picture?

a   b   c   d   e   f

Which words?

Write in the missing word for each of these episode titles, using one of the words opposite.

JAKE **LUNCH**
PHONE **HANNAHS**

1 Don't Stop 'Til You Get the ....

2 It's the End of the .... As We Know It

3 You Give .... a Bad Name

4 Torn Between Two ....

Shady lady

Can you match the correct Hannah shadow to the main picture?

a   b   c

31

Answers on page 67.

What's your Number?

Use numerology to discover what Miley's birth date says about her — and find out what your birth date says about you, too!

Calculate your number

Miley was born on 23rd November 1992

To calculate your special number, add up all of the numbers in your birth date. So Miley would add up the following — 2+3 (day of birth) + 1+1 (month of birth — November is the 11th month) + 1+9+9+2 (year of birth). It adds up to 28, so she would then add 2+8, which equals 10. This is still a double digit, so as 1+0 = 1, Miley's numerological number is 1.

Work out what your friends' and families' numbers are too. Does it sound like them? It's spookily accurate!

Numbers explained ...

1

Number 1s are competitive people, who are very likely to succeed in life. You love the idea of being your own boss and adore being in the limelight.

2

You're a big music fan and are also likely to be a very talented musician. Your friends and family are very important to you.

3

You're warm and friendly, with a great sense of humour. You're a brilliant writer and are into visiting new places.

4

If you're a number 4, you're a gentle person, who loves animals, exploring the countryside and walking by the sea.

5

Popular number 5s love spending time with other peeps – and other peeps love spending time with them! You always stand up for what you believe in.

6

You're the organiser in your group of friends - whether it's a day out or a sleepover. You're generous with your time and friendship.

7

Number 7s are incredibly creative and interested in loads of different things. They tend to have a big group of friends.

8

There's a lot of hidden depth to number 8s. There are only a few people who know you really well. You're ambitious and know what you want.

9

Animal lovers, number 9s are also adventurous peeps who love sport. You're full of life and love the idea of being famous one day!

How to Party Like Hannah Montana!

Follow Hannah's top tips for the perfect party.

Outfit-tastic

Follow Hannah's example and choose a cool party dress to make you stand out from the crowd. This is especially important if you're hosting the party!

Listen up, y'all! Do not wear an old grey sweater like my pa here!

Huh, what's wrong with my sweater?!

That means you're leaving, cuz!

Bye, TJ!

Great guests

It's very important that you invite your fave peeps to make your party really rockin'. Leave anyone rude or annoying off the guest list!

Yummy food

If you've got a pesky brother or sister hanging around, lay down some ground rules on what they can and can't do. Otherwise, they may end up stealing your food!

Music makes it

Good music makes your party go with a bang! Hike up the fun factor with karaoke – take it in turns to sing Hannah's greatest hits!

Fun, fun, fun!

Make sure you have plenty of games to play so that everyone gets involved and gets to know each other.

What's your Party

Find out what kind of party is totally you!

START

When it's karaoke time you ...

Jump up to the stage! →

Hide quietly in the corner ↓

You prefer doing things with a big group of pals ...

Always! →

Sometimes ↓

Your fave thing about sleepovers are ...

The games! →

The gossiping! ↓

Are you always the first on the dancefloor?

For sure! →

No way! ↓

Fancy dress parties are ...

Great! ↗

Grrr! →

You absolutely love pampering yourself ...

It's not your fave thing in the world

Totally!

Style?

Performing rocks your world ...

Without a doubt!

You can take it or leave it

Wearing wigs is totally ...

Rad!

Not me!

You and your BFF are always ...

Giggling together

Telling each other your secrets

Karaoke time!

Look out everyone, there's a karaoke queen about! You love to perform, so a karaoke party is a dream for you! Make sure you belt out a few Hannah songs at your cool sing-a-long party too!

Fancy dress fun

You're absolutely mad for fancy dress! You love giggling with your friends and think dressing up is awesome! Dress up as Hannah and Lola with your BFF at your next fancy dress party!

Super sleepover

Bonding with your BFF is mega important to you, so a sleepover party suits you best. Giggle, chat and gossip while you watch your fave Hannah Montana episodes — like 'California Screamin'! (above).

37

The Dice of Destiny

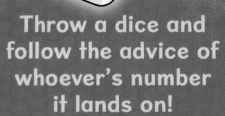

Throw a dice and follow the advice of whoever's number it lands on!

"Have a good giggle with your BFF today!"

"Wear a cool hair accessory, in honour of Lola!"

"Tell your BFF ten reasons why they're amazing!"

"Make up a dance routine to your fave Hannah song!"

"Customise an old top to make it brand-new again!"

"Come up with five impressions to show your pals!"

38

Superstar Secret Code

Use the key to unscramble the secret messages that Miley and Lilly are trying to send each other.

Code

♪ = a ♥ = e ✿ = m ★ = t

From: Miley
To: Lilly
Cc:

Subject: Read this NOW!

Miley: Lilly, our pl♪n work♥d!

Lilly: Which pl♪n? W♥ h♪ve so ✿♪ny!

Miley: Dad is ★♪king Lori on ♪ d♪★♥!

Lilly: ★h♪★ is ♪✿♪zing! Hmm, w♥ ✿us♥ giv♥ hi✿ ♪dvic♥ on wh♪★ ★o w♥♪r ★hough.

Miley: ★o★♪lly! H♥y, l♥★'s l♥♪v♥ ♪n ou★fi★ ou★ for hi✿ on his b♥d!

Lilly: Do you ★hink h♥'ll g♥t th♥ hin★?

Miley: Y♥♥ D♪wgi♥s, h♥'d b♥★★♥r or Lori's gonn♪ b♥ s♪ying "By♥ By♥ Robby R♪y!" quick♥r th♪n i★ ★♪k♥s him ★o ♥♪★ ♪ pi♥!

39

Answers on page 68.

The Jackson and Robby Show!

Miley's brother Jackson and her dad Robby totally rock! Find out more about them here ...

Big brother Jackson

Jackson is Miley's older brother. They fight like cat and dog, but would do anything for each other. Miley faced a dilemma when Jackson begged her to tell his girlfriend Siena about her secret alter-ego, but she did it in the end.

Jackson and Rico

Cheeky Rico (Jackson's ex boss) is constantly coming up with ways to make Jackson's life difficult! But sometimes Jackson manages to get the last laugh – like when Rico taunted him for not being able to grow a moustache and Jackson showed Rico pics of his family going bald at a young age!

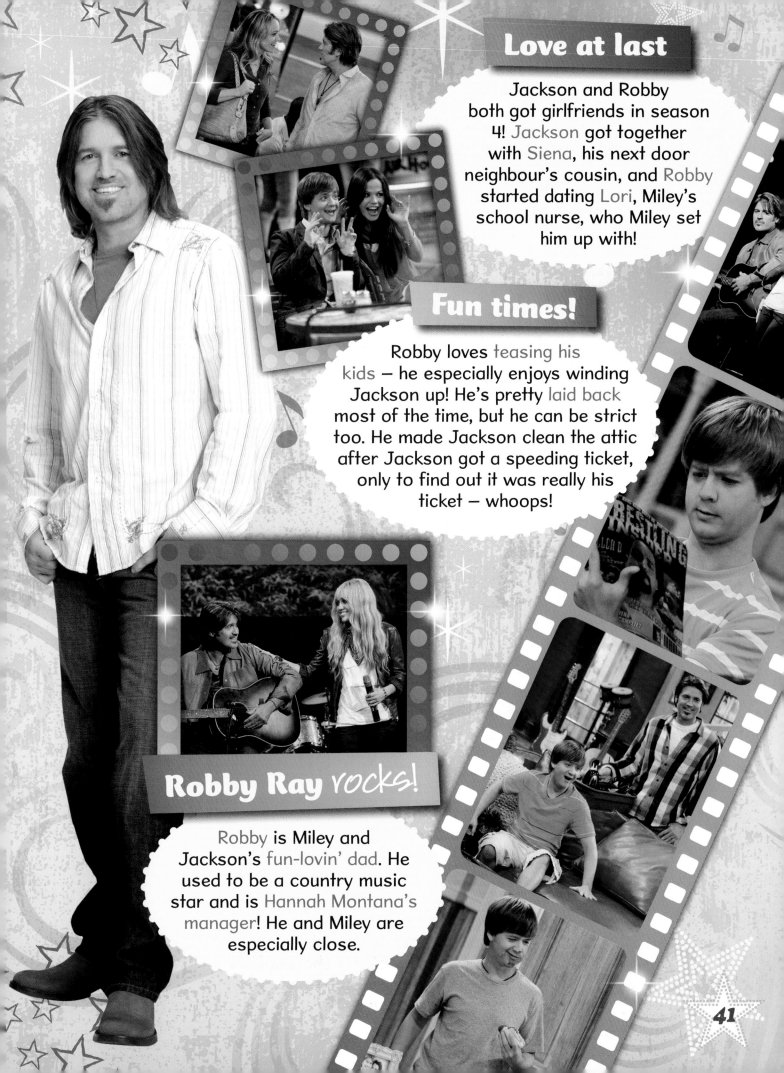

Love at last

Jackson and Robby both got girlfriends in season 4! Jackson got together with Siena, his next door neighbour's cousin, and Robby started dating Lori, Miley's school nurse, who Miley set him up with!

Fun times!

Robby loves teasing his kids – he especially enjoys winding Jackson up! He's pretty laid back most of the time, but he can be strict too. He made Jackson clean the attic after Jackson got a speeding ticket, only to find out it was really his ticket – whoops!

Robby Ray rocks!

Robby is Miley and Jackson's fun-lovin' dad. He used to be a country music star and is Hannah Montana's manager! He and Miley are especially close.

It's Show Time!

Follow Hannah's guide on how to put together the perfect show.

The stage

Feeling creative? Design a banner to sit across the top of the stage like this one. You could write, 'Hannah Montana rocks!' and cover it in glitter!

The right music

Think about what kind of show you want to put on and make sure that your music matches. This particular song wouldn't have worked with a big band!

Get dancing

This song didn't need any big dance moves, but the other number Hannah performed in this episode, did. So make sure you get a good dance routine sorted out. Nothing too tricky though, you still need to be able to sing!

Lively lighting

Use fairy lights to re-create this awesome lighting look when you put on a show at home. It'll create a similar spotlight effect.

Rehearsal time

Make sure that you rehearse as much as possible so that you feel really confident when you get on that stage. You want the audience to love you, just like these guys love Hannah!

Cool costume

Grab a plain Tee, but liven it up with a bright jacket, rockin' accessories and gorgeous shoes! Don't forget the popstar attitude!

The Mega Mate Challenge

Follow these top tips for Hannah Montana fun with your BFF!

Get giggling

 1 Try on some cool outfits – the more Hannah/Lola the better! ☐

 2 Make up a dance routine to your favourite Hannah Montana song. ☐

 3 Act out the scene from 'Sweet Home Hannah Montana' on pages 46 to 49! ☐

 4 Both write a story about what you think Miley and the gang will do next. ☐

Sleepover Fun

Miley and Lilly are on a permanent sleepover now that Lilly shares her bedroom!

Have a sleepover with your best friend and play some Hannah Montana inspired games! You could play, "Guess the Hannah Montana character", where one of you chooses a character and the other person has to ask questions to find out who it is. The catch is, they can only answer 'yes' or 'no' to the questions!

Make her a friendship bracelet

You'll need:
ribbon, cool beads

 1 Tie a knot 10cm before the end of the ribbon.

 2 Thread your beads onto the ribbon. Choose cool colours!

 3 When there's enough beads to go round your wrist, tie another knot to keep the beads in place.

 4 Make yourself a matching one and then give the other one to her!

Test your knowledge

See how much you know about your best friend's fave Hannah Montana things!

★ Who's her fave character? (Apart from Hannah!)

★ What's her fave episode ever?

★ Which character makes her giggle the most?

★ What's her fave Hannah Montana song?

Sweet Home Hannah Montana

Act out these scenes from, 'Sweet Home Hannah Montana', following the script below.

Scene 1

THE STEWARTS' SITTING ROOM

The Stewarts and Lilly have moved to an ace ranch house in Malibu. But unfortunately, Robby had Hannah's old bedroom from when she was six moved up to Mailbu too – and four school friends have just come over to see it!

Joannie: Stewart! This house is unbelievable!

Sarah: It's like my dream house! Except it doesn't have solar panels, a rainwater reclamation system and it isn't made out of used tyres, but other than that, it's perfect!

Joannie: (Said sarcastically) Way to bring down room, Sarah. And FYI, a tree never died to make a breath mint. (Gestures to her own mouth.)

Sarah: (Brings hand to mouth in shock) That's organic broccoli!

Miley: You know what? She's right, she's right! This house is an energy sucking eye-sore, I am ashamed for you guys to see it. (Miley and Lilly start moving them towards the door, open the door and gesture the others towards it.) You guys should just, ya know, I think you guys should leave.

Joannie: Oh come on! Let us at least see your bedroom! (Looks around at her three friends who nod in agreement.)

Miley: Uhhhhhhhh, (looking at Lilly, desperately trying to think of a way to put them off) We would ...

Lilly: (in agreement with Miley) Mmm-hmm!

Miley: But Lilly's gotta get down to her new job at the Pier!

Robby: (coming in from the kitchen) Mile! What's the rush? You've got time to show them your bedroom!

Miley: (Aggressively) She has to go to work!

Lilly: (Hysterically) I have to go to work!

Joannie: (Coming off her mobile phone, looking annoyed) Oh man! My stupid little brother is sick and now I can't have my – (turns to point to Sarah) call it a slumber party and I'll pound your face in – sleepover, this weekend.

Miley: Too bad!

Lilly: What a shame!

Miley: We can't live in the past!

Lilly: Let's go to the pier!

Robby: Hey, I gotta a good idea! Why don't you have your party here?

Miley: (looking horrified) Didn't-see-that-one-coming-Daddy-say what?!

Joannie: (Excited) Really, Mr Stewart?

Lilly: (In a telling-off tone) Really, Mr Stewart?

Robby: Absolutely! There's no better way to break in a new house, than a good old-fashioned sleepover! (Miley looks really worried as Robby taps her on the arm.) Besides, it's a great way to kick off your senior year!

Miley: (With the same worried expression on her face) You betcha!

Scene 2

THE STEWARTS' SITTING ROOM

After Miley spots a hideous shirt at the pier that reminds her of an old shirt of her dad's, she realises that she can use it to show her dad that just because you really loved something in the past, it doesn't mean you'll still love it in the future – like her bedroom! So she gives it to her dad who at first tells her that he loves it ...

Miley: If you don't tell me you hate it right now, we're going to walk out that door, mister. (Gestures towards the door.)

Robby: (Looks sadly down at his shirt) Alright, I hate this shirt.

Miley: And now you realise that ... (tries to encourage him to say it!)

Robby: (Looking slightly confused) I *really* hate this shirt?

Lilly: (Exclaiming loudly) NO! Miley hates her bedroom! When she said she wanted to wrap it up and ship it out here, she didn't mean it literally! I mean, we're girls, we say things we don't mean – get a clue!

Miley: (Puts her hand towards her chest) That's the hardest thing I've ever had to say.

Robby: (They all move towards the couch) Well, why didn't you just tell me you didn't like your bedroom?

Miley: Cos, I didn't wanna hurt your feelings.

Robby: You know you can tell me anything, I'll always understand. As long as it's said with love and (turns towards Lilly) sensitivity.

Lilly: (Looking apologetic) Sorry!

Miley: I didn't want to come off ungrateful, because you do so much for me.

Robby: And I get the feeling, I'm getting ready to do just a little more.

Lilly: (Pleadingly) Please!

Miley: So a complete bedroom make-over?

Robby: Why not? We can design it together! (Starts to get up off the sofa.)

Miley: (Pulling Robby back down) OR, I will design it and you'll write the cheque.

Robby: Even better!

Scene 3

BLUE JEANS' BARN

Miley calls Joannie to cancel the sleepover and Lilly and her start discussing how to re-design her room. Jackson walks in and burps loudly, making Miley and Lilly realise that they'll still have to live next door to him! But then there's always the barn …

Lilly: (Holding a clipboard and pen.) Well it smells better than Jackson's meatball burp, but not by much!

Miley: Are you kidding? After we're done with this place, it's gonna be rad!

Lilly: (Waving her pen around.) OK, well, I just have one rule (walks up to Blue Jeans and points her pencil at him). He's gotta turn around when I change!

Miley: Don't worry, I'll move him into the other barn. (Looks at Blue Jeans) Because you're a horse, you live in a barn, we've been over this!

THE END

Why we love Hannah Montana

There are so many reasons why Miley/Hannah rocks!
Check out some of them here.

Brilliant best friend

Miley's such a great best friend, that she's even invited Lilly to live with her and share her room!

Double the fun!

She lives a secret double life that most girls can only dream of — she really does have the best of both worlds!

Loadsa laughs

Miley has an amazingly infectious laugh and she's totally hilarious too! She makes us LOL at least 15 times every episode!

Awesome bedroom

Miley's bedroom in season 4 is super-cool! She designed it with Lilly and it's full of ace features including Hannah's hidden closet!

Cool clothes

Whether she's in Miley mode or glamming it up as Hannah, this girl's got rockin' dress sense!

50

Amazing daughter

Miley and her dad, Robby, are really close, which is lucky, as he's Hannah's manager too!

She's no diva

She might be a world-famous superstar, but Miley's still the same down-to-earth girl she's always been!

Super songs

We love Hannah's music — she's a brilliant performer and her songs get stuck in our heads for days and days!

51

Meet the Rest of the Gang!

Here's Oliver, Rico, TJ, Siena and Lori!

Smoken' Oken!

Oliver Oken is the other BFF in Miley and Lilly's life. He's always cheery and optimistic, and he's also a fantastic singer. He made the semi-finals of 'America's Top Talent' and went on tour with the band he joined!

Meet Lori

Lori is the school nurse at Seaview. She's kind and caring, and she goes out with Robby Ray in 'Hannah Montana Forever'. Miley sneakily sets them up together by ringing her dad saying that Lilly's got cold sweats, so he turns up to collect "ill" Lilly and meets Lori!

It's Rico!

Rico Suave is the money-mad, super-brainy owner of Rico's Surf Shack. He's two years younger than Miley, Lilly and Oliver, but he's in the same year at school as them because he's so clever! One of Rico's great pleasures in life is taunting Jackson and Oliver.

Super Siena

Siena is Jackson's gorgeous girlfriend who he meets when the Stewarts move to Malibu. She's fun and cool, but she nearly breaks up with Jackson when she thinks he's dating Hannah Montana. Once Miley comes clean, it means there's another person in on the secret.

53

Hannah: True or False?

We've heard all sorts of stories about Hannah, but what's true and what's false?

Hannah went to great lengths to try and stop Jake marrying Traci.

True!

Hannah went to Las Vegas to stop them getting married. She tried to ruin the wedding, only to find out that it was a stunt for the TV Series 'Gotcha' – cringe!

Hannah went on a date with Rico.

False!

Although she did kind of go on a date with him when Johnny Collins won a date with her at an auction! Rico went along too, after Hannah was told that a date with both of them would raise twice as much money for charity!

Hannah has a vacuum-packed emergency Hannah kit.

True!

Miley used it to transform into Hannah in, 'Sweet Home Hannah Montana'!

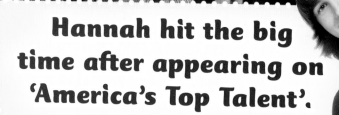

Hannah hit the big time after appearing on 'America's Top Talent'.

False!

Hannah was a judge on 'America's Top Talent'. She found it mega awkward having to judge Oliver on it!

Hannah performed in front of the Queen.

True!

Hannah performed in front of the Queen and her granddaughter in, 'Grandma Don't Let Your Babies Grow Up to Play Favorites'.

Everyone totally ignored Hannah when she joined Seaview.

False!

Yeah, right! Everyone was totally star-struck when Hannah registered at Seaview, (because Miley hadn't registered in time, she registered as Hannah) even Principal Luger!

55

Hair Flair

How quickly can you solve these hair-raising puzzles?

Mini wordsearch

Find the hair related words below in this wordsearch.

BRUSH
PONYTAIL
WAVY
PLAIT
BOB
WIG

```
G A P O L Y C L
M B O Y M C H H
P O N E R C E W
E D Y R B O B A
N I T I G U R V
X L A B D I U Y
Y W I G U H S O
N P L A I T H N
H T R A C I N M
```

Choose your fave Hannah/Miley, Lilly/Lola hairstyle from these cool pics.

Hannah's cool waves

Miley's up-do

Miley's maze

Miley's having a bad hair day! Can you guide her through the maze, collecting all the hairbrushes along the way?

Start

Finish

Answers on page 68.

Lilly's cute plaits

Lola's funky bob

57

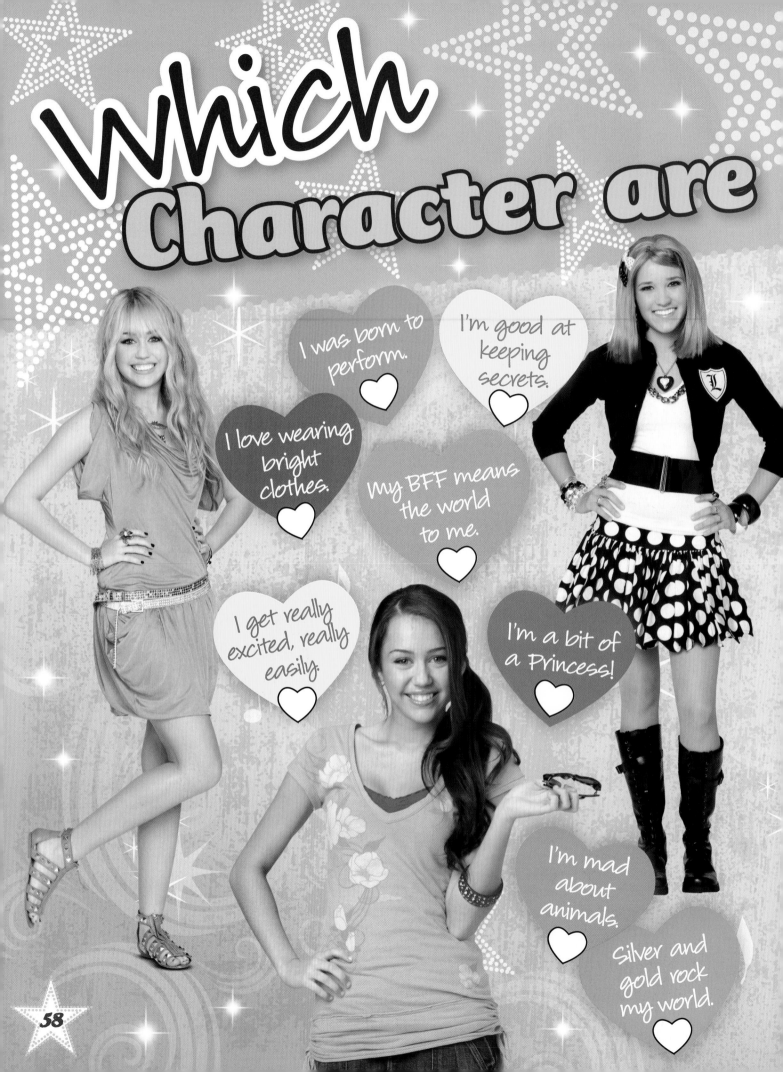

Which Character are

I was born to perform.

I'm good at keeping secrets.

I love wearing bright clothes.

My BFF means the world to me.

I get really excited, really easily.

I'm a bit of a Princess!

I'm mad about animals.

Silver and gold rock my world.

58

You?

Tick the six statements that you agree with the most to find out!

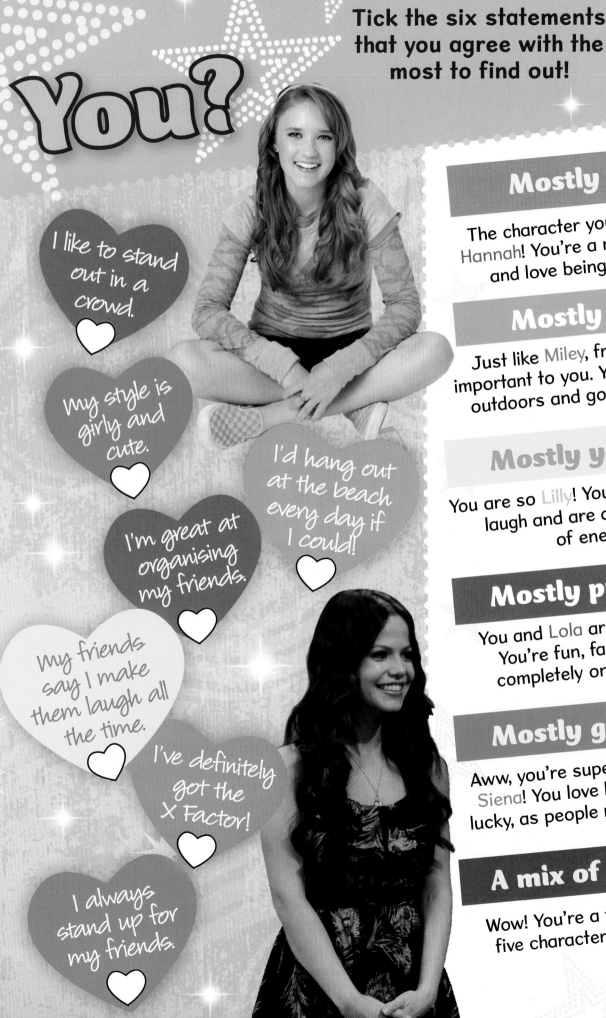

I like to stand out in a crowd.

My style is girly and cute.

I'd hang out at the beach every day if I could!

I'm great at organising my friends.

My friends say I make them laugh all the time.

I've definitely got the X Factor!

I always stand up for my friends.

Mostly pinks:

The character you're most like is Hannah! You're a natural superstar and love being on the stage!

Mostly blues:

Just like Miley, friends are really important to you. You also love being outdoors and going to the beach.

Mostly yellows:

You are so Lilly! You make everyone laugh and are a real bundle of energy!

Mostly purples:

You and Lola are total twins! You're fun, fabulous and completely one of a kind!

Mostly greens:

Aww, you're super-cute, just like Siena! You love being adored — lucky, as people really adore you!

A mix of colours:

Wow! You're a total mix of all five characters — how cool!

Montana Montage

Check out a few of Miley's fave pics from her photo albums!

A new star is born

Hannah and Lola

When Lilly discovered Miley's amazing secret, she came up with the alter ego, Lola Luftnagle, to help keep Hannah's true identity a secret. She travels to events with Hannah, posing as her assistant. From the first season to the fourth, they've had a ton of fun together!

More fabulous outfits!

Robby Ray gets practical!

At the Stewarts

Miley and her family have always lived in a really cool house, but at the start of season 4 they moved to the ultimate house - a Malibu Ranch! Lilly's also living with them now, so they're roomies as well as BFFs!

BFFs forever

Friends in high places

Not only did Hannah once perform in front of the Queen, but she knows the President too! She called in a favour from President Obama when she wasn't registered in time for senior year and he was very happy to help!

Starting out

Hello, Obama!

Just Jake

Miley met Jake when he enrolled at Seaview Middle School. A teen actor, Miley was the only person who wasn't star-struck by his celebrity status. They had an on/off romance for a while.

Just before Hannah socked it to him!

Early days

Daddy's girl

Although Miley and her dad get on really well, they still hurt each other's feelings by mistake sometimes. But Miley organising a concert in honour of the military after realising how lucky she is to still have Robby around, is a pretty cool way of showing she cares!

Daddy dearest

A top performance

Odd One Out

Can you spot which picture
is the odd one out and why?

Answer on page 68.

Song Switch

The titles on Hannah's song list are jumbled up. Can you unscramble them and write the correct song titles below them?

a ear ouy deary (tarruseps)

b dene a tilelt oevl

c anong teg hsti

d l'il wyalsa bemermer uoy

e ueq reas

f raynidor lrig

Answers on page 68.

Hannah Montana Forever!

Do ya think you know everything about Hannah Montana? Test yourself with our awesome quiz!

1 Who did Oliver have a crush on right at the beginning of season one?

a) Miley ☐
b) Lilly ☐
c) Hannah ☐

2 Who are Amber and Ashley?

a) Miley's best friends from Tennessee ☐
b) The school mean girls ☐
c) Miley's cousins ☐

3 Who's Aunt Dolly?

a) Miley's godmother ☐
b) Robby's sister ☐
c) Lilly's mom ☐

4 What was the name of Jake's biggest TV show?

a) Vampire High ☐
b) Zombie High ☐
c) Attack of the Zombie Slayers ☐

5 The first ever episode of Hannah Montana was called ...

a) Lilly, Do You Want a Sweet? ☐
b) Lilly, Do You Want to Know a Secret? ☐
c) Lilly, Do You Want to Get On Up on the Dancefloor? ☐

6 Miley got jealous when this person got on really well with the Jonas Brothers ...

a) Jackson ☐
b) Oliver ☐
c) Robby ☐

7 Who got cast in a film with Jake, much to Miley's annoyance?

a) Mikayla ☐
b) Traci ☐
c) Mamaw ☐

8 Complete the season 2 song title. Life's ...

a) Great! ☐
b) Just not Fair ☐
c) What You Make It ☐

9 Which former enemy does Lilly become friends with after Oliver dates her?

a) Joannie ☐
b) Sarah ☐
c) Mikayla ☐

10 Who is Isis?

a) Yet another of Miley's cousins! ☐
b) Hannah's idol – an older superstar ☐
c) A woman who Robby briefly dates in season 2 ☐

11 What put Miley off Connor, a cute guy she met in season 3?

a) His bad hair ☐
b) His lack of height ☐
c) His terrible clothes ☐

12 Who did Jackson use as a dummy in a ventriloquist's show?

a) Rico ☐
b) Robby ☐
c) Miley ☐

13 What did Hannah lose when she was on the S.S. Tipton, which she then blamed for a run of bad luck?

a) A necklace Lilly gave her ☐
b) An anklet which belonged to her mother ☐
c) Her lucky scarf ☐

14 Which Hannah song did Oliver perform on 'America's Top Talent'?

a) 'Let's Get Crazy' ☐
b) 'The Best of Both Worlds' ☐
c) 'Let's Do This' ☐

15 Who does Miley dream about that first makes her think she might want to move back to Tennessee?

a) Her mom ☐
b) Mamaw ☐
c) Blue Jeans ☐

16 How does Siena know TJ?

a) He's her old neighbour ☐
b) He's her cousin ☐
c) He's her dad ☐

17 What's the crazy coaster cackle?

a) Robby's yelp when someone doesn't use a coaster on his fave table ☐

b) Robby's mad laugh when he rides a rollercoaster ☐

c) A new dance craze that Robby invented ☐

18 What sidetracks Jackson from reading a classic book? (To impress Siena!)

a) His wrestling magazines ☐

b) America's Top Talent on the TV ☐

c) Nothing could ever distract Jackson from reading a classic book! ☐

19 Where is Hannah when inspiration strikes for 'Gonna Get This'?

a) The pier ☐

b) Seaview High cafeteria ☐

c) On the beach ☐

20 What do Jackson, Siena and Rico NOT dress up as during 'I'll Always Remember You'?

a) Mime artists ☐

b) Animals ☐

c) Hannah, Lola and Mike ☐

How did you do?

Check the answers on page 68, add up your points and then check out your score below.

0 – 7 Better luck next time! Re-read the annual from start to finish and then re-test yourself!

8 – 14 Not bad! Re-watch a few of your fave Hannah Montana DVDs and your score will shoot up!

15 – 20 You're fan-tastic! What you don't know about Hannah, obviously isn't worth knowing!

Answers on page 68.

The Answers

1) Jackson
2) Robby
3) Miley 4) Siena
5) Oliver 6) Rico 7) Lilly

Across:

1) Gonna Get This
3) School nurse
4) Truscott 5) Bikini
7) Standley 11) Blue Jeans
12) Judge Me 13) Rico
14) Mikayla

Down:

2) Sweet niblets
6) Goodbye 7) Supergirl
8) Jesse 9) Spiders
10) Van Horn

Jigsaw puzzler!
1 = f, 2 = d, 3 = a, 4 = e

Which words?
1) Phone 2) Jake
3) Lunch 4) Hannahs

Shady lady
The answer is b

Superstar Secret Code 39

Miley: Lilly, our plan worked!

Lilly: Which plan? We have so many!

Miley: Dad is taking Lori on a date!

Lilly: That is amazing! Hmm, we must give him advice on what to wear though.

Miley: Totally! Hey, let's leave an outfit out for him on his bed!

Lilly: Do you think he'll get the hint?

Miley: Yee dawgies, he'd better or Lori's gonna be saying, "Bye Bye Robby Ray!" quicker than it takes him to eat a pie!

Odd One Out 62

Picture 4

Song Switch 63

a) Are You Ready (Superstar)
b) Need A Little Love
c) Gonna Get This
d) I'll Always Remember You
e) Que Sera
f) Ordinary Girl

Hair Flair 56

Mini wordsearch

Miley's maze

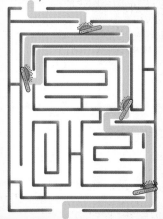

Hannah Montana Forever! 64-66

1) c, 2) b, 3) a, 4) b, 5) b, 6) c, 7) a, 8) c, 9) a, 10) b, 11) b, 12) a, 13) b, 14) c, 15) c, 16) b, 17) b, 18) a, 19) a, 20) b

THE OFFICIAL MAGAZINE

Don't miss it!

Packed with...

fun facts
quizzes
posters
fashion tips
competitions
interviews
with the stars!

ON SALE EVERY MONTH!

FREE GIFT EVERY ISSUE!

Available at all good supermarkets and newsagents

© Disney